THE
RAINFOREST
Colouring Book

Enter the short URL or scan this QR code
into your tablet, laptop or computer to
listen to relaxing rainforest sounds for a
truly immersive colouring experience.

https://youtu.be/-IAfg_Iy7n8

CARLTON
BOOKS

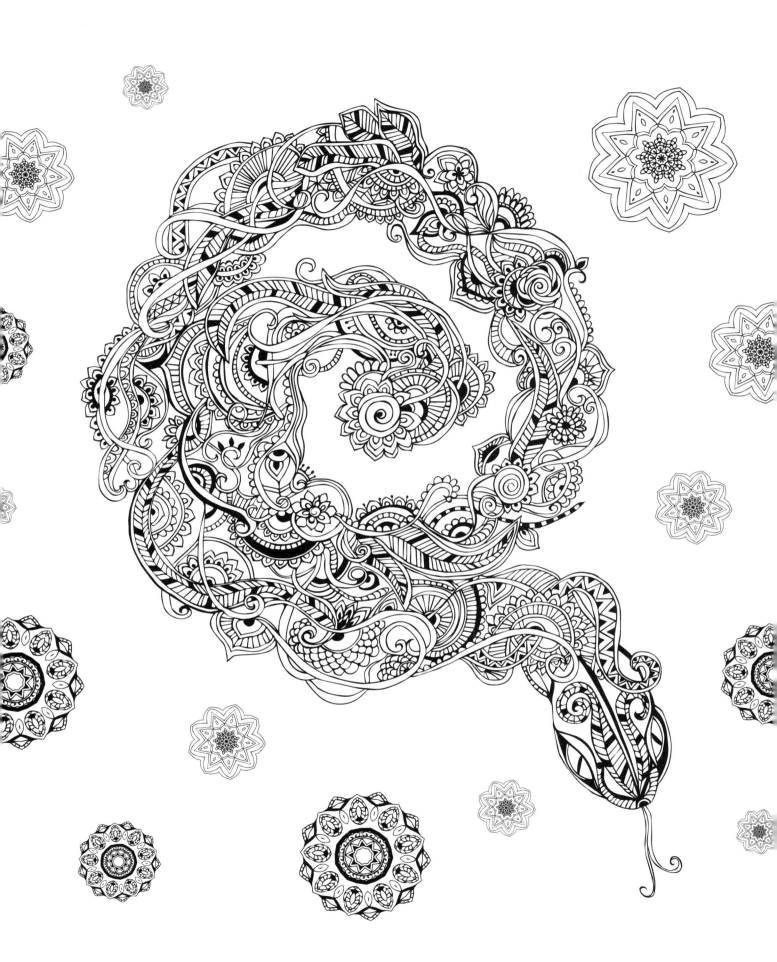

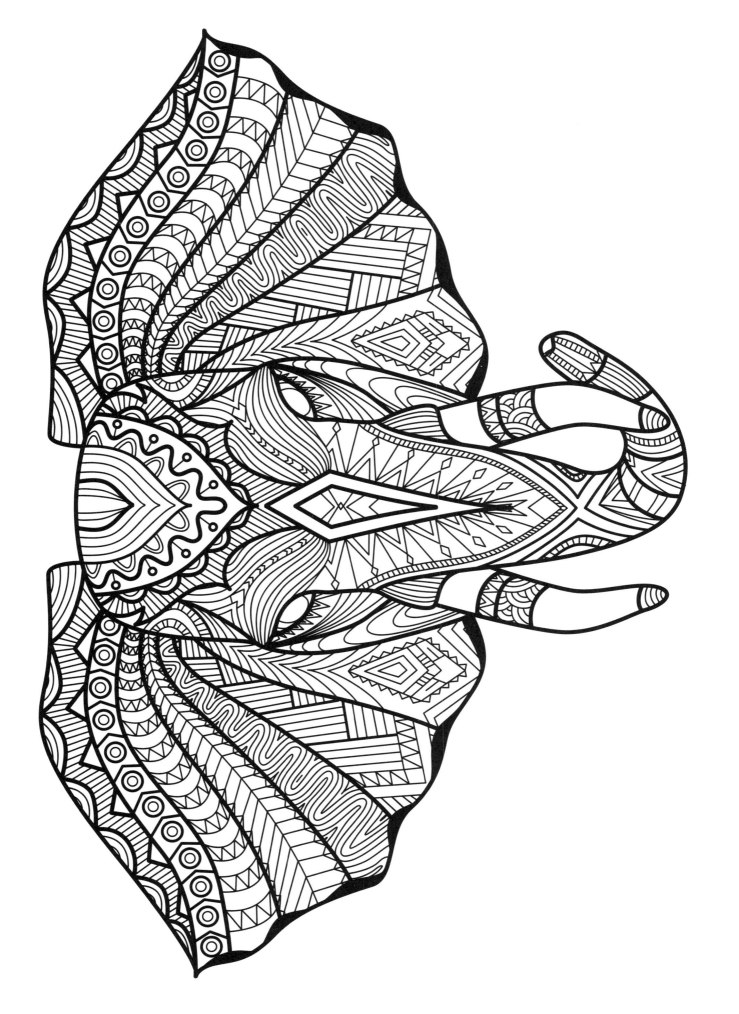

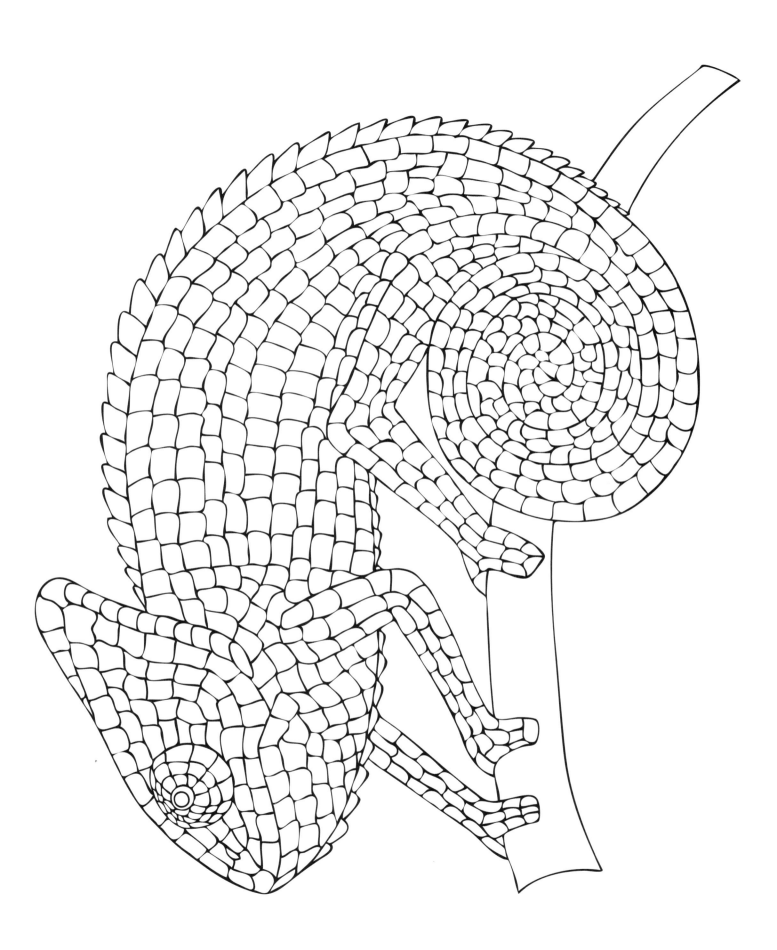

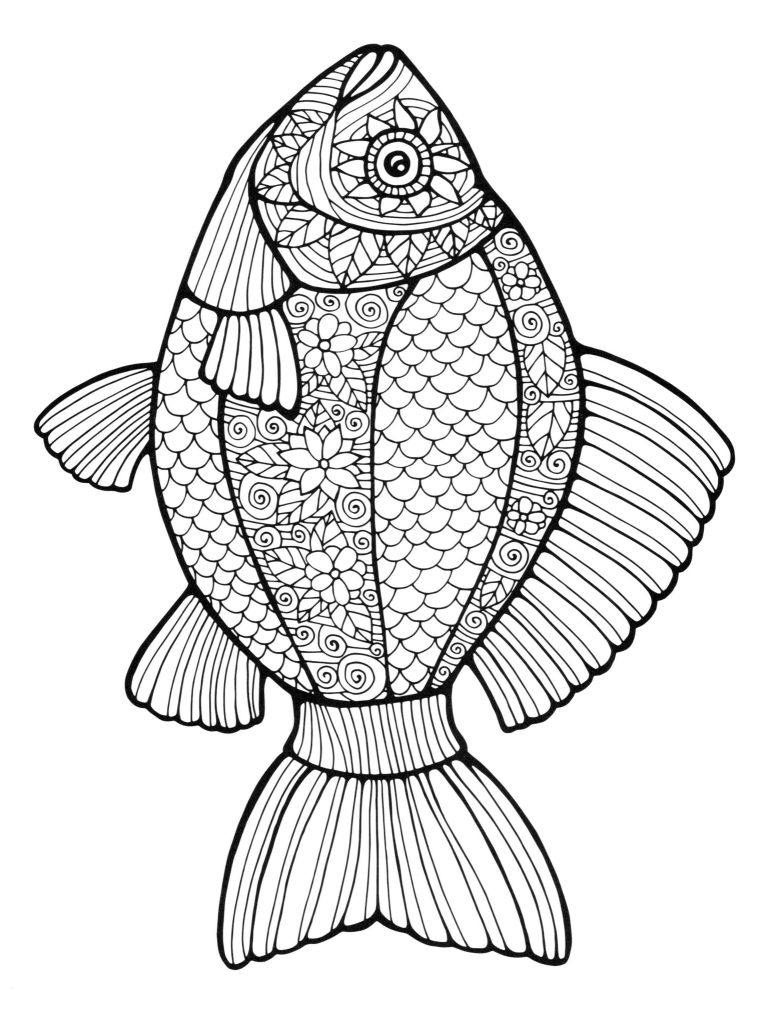

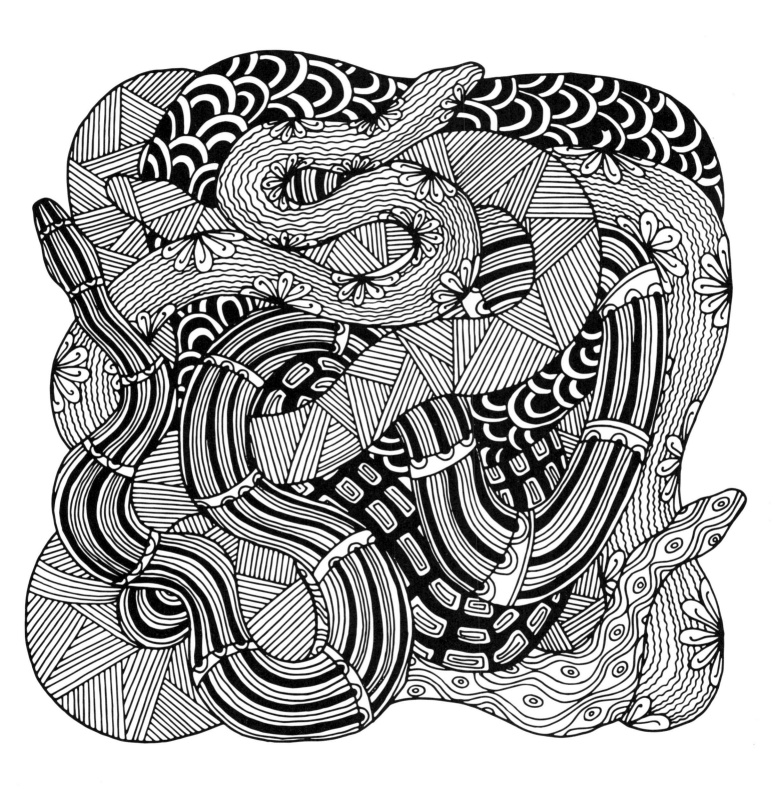

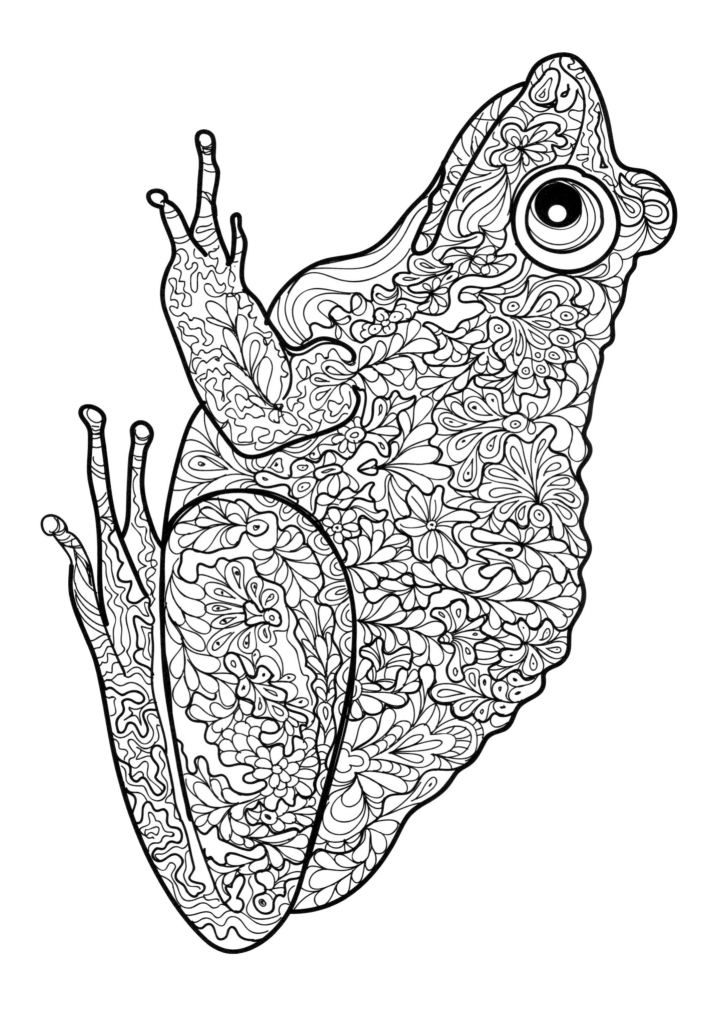

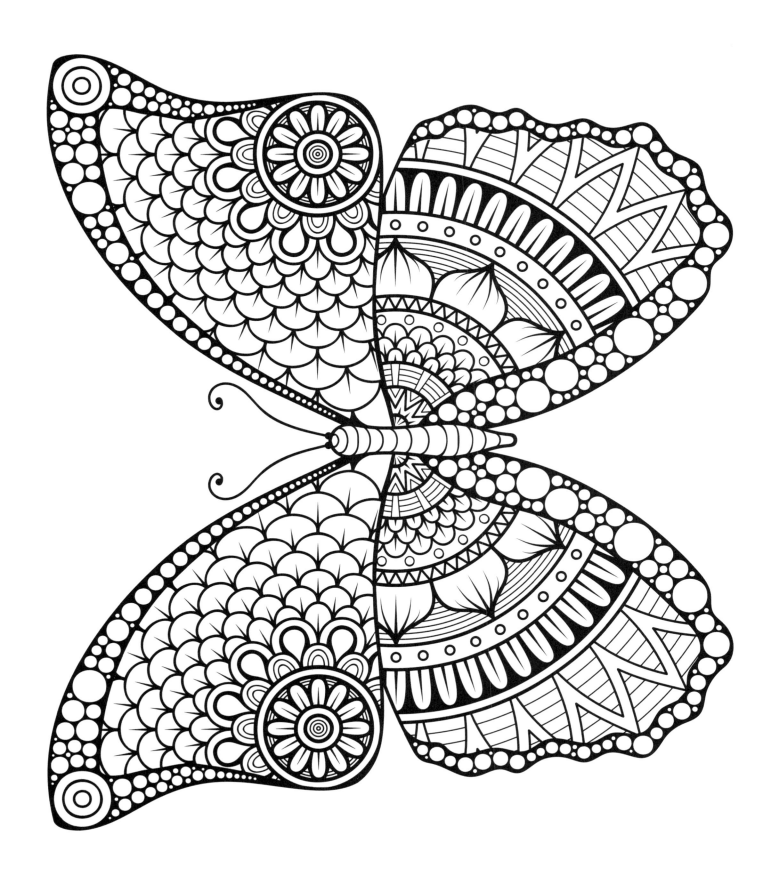

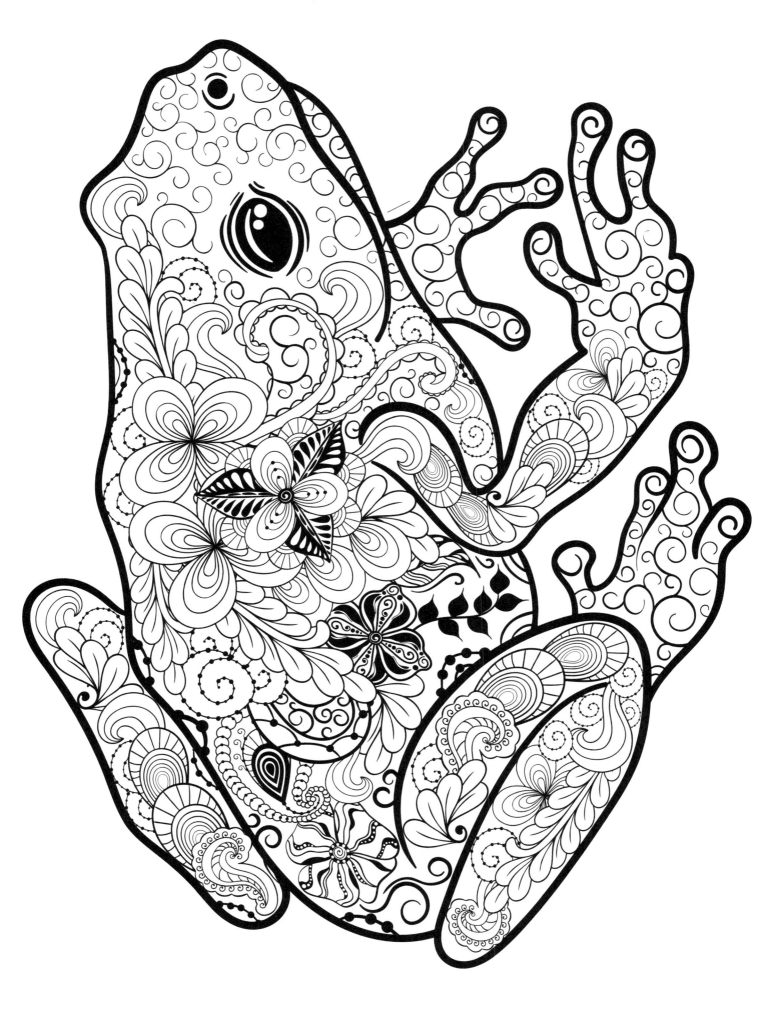

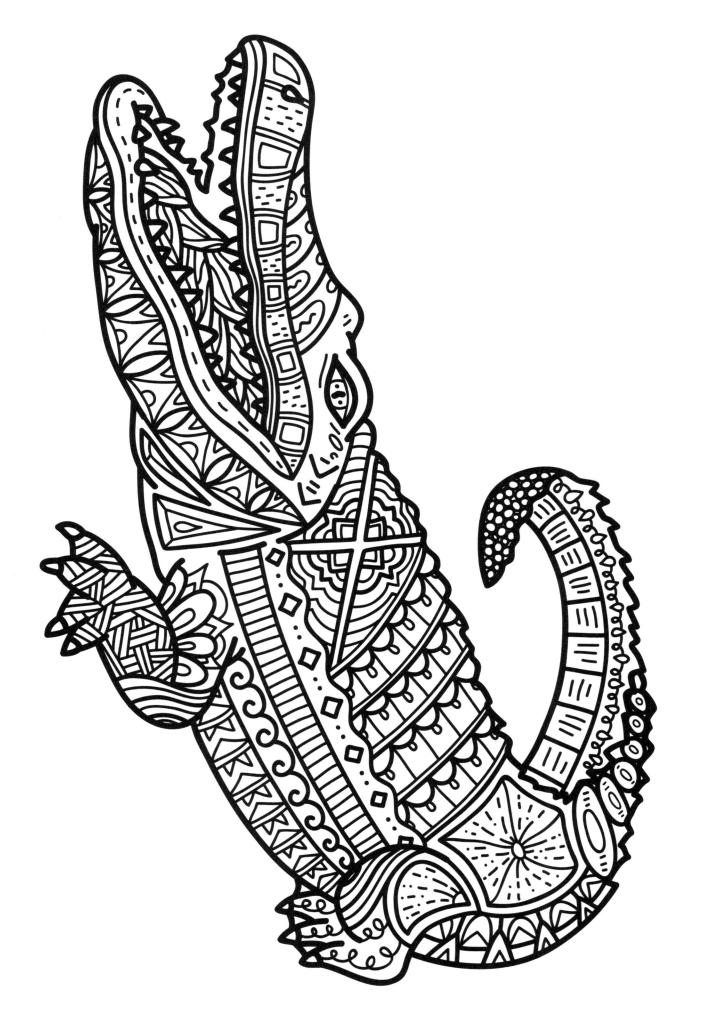

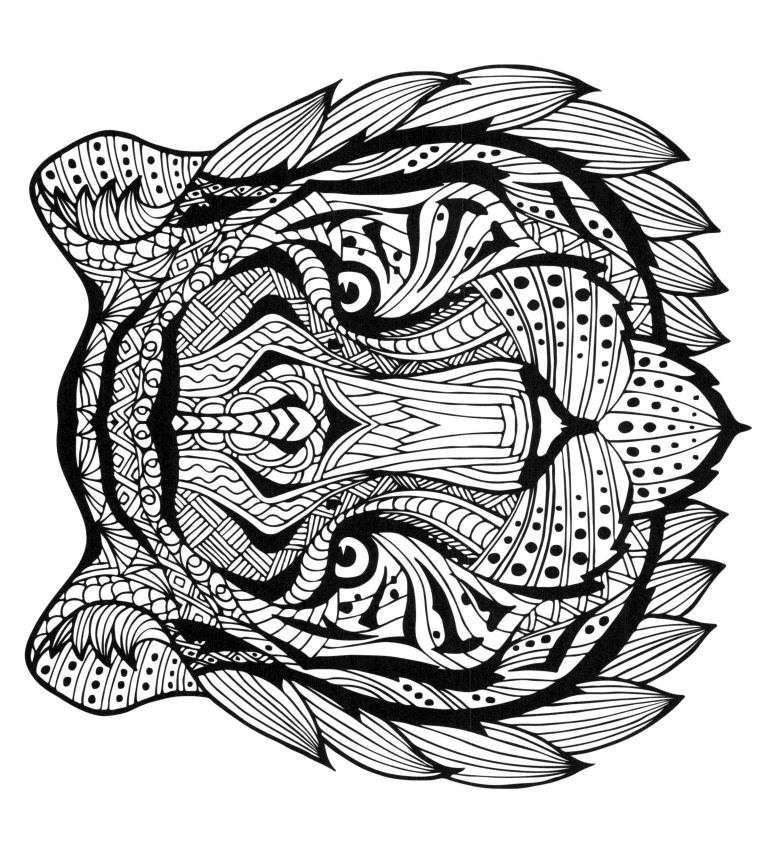

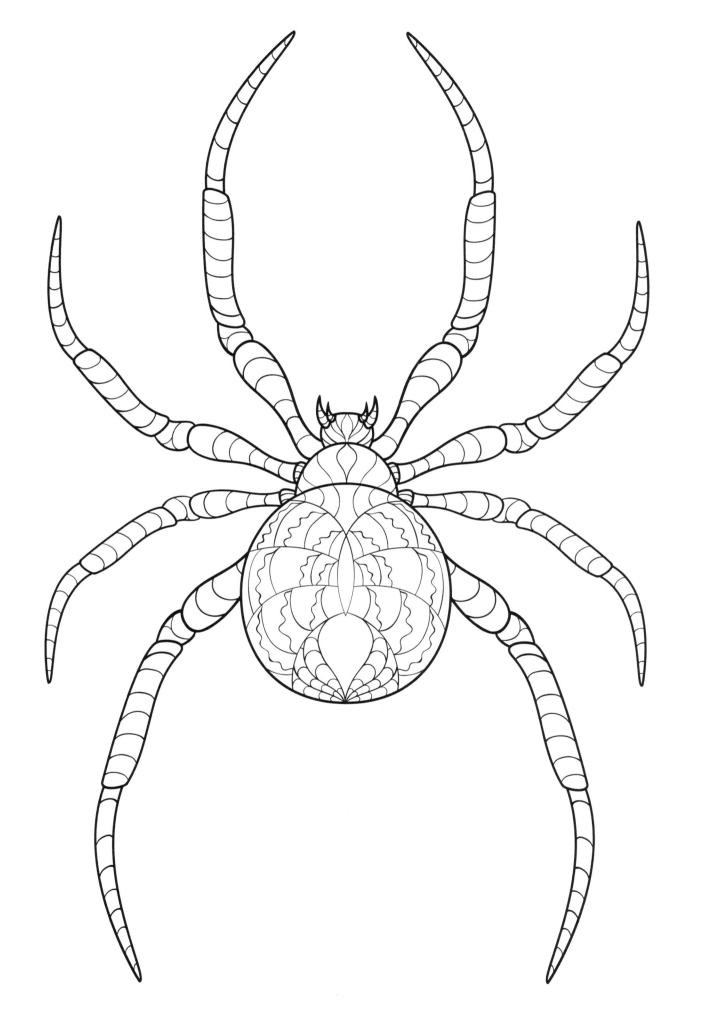

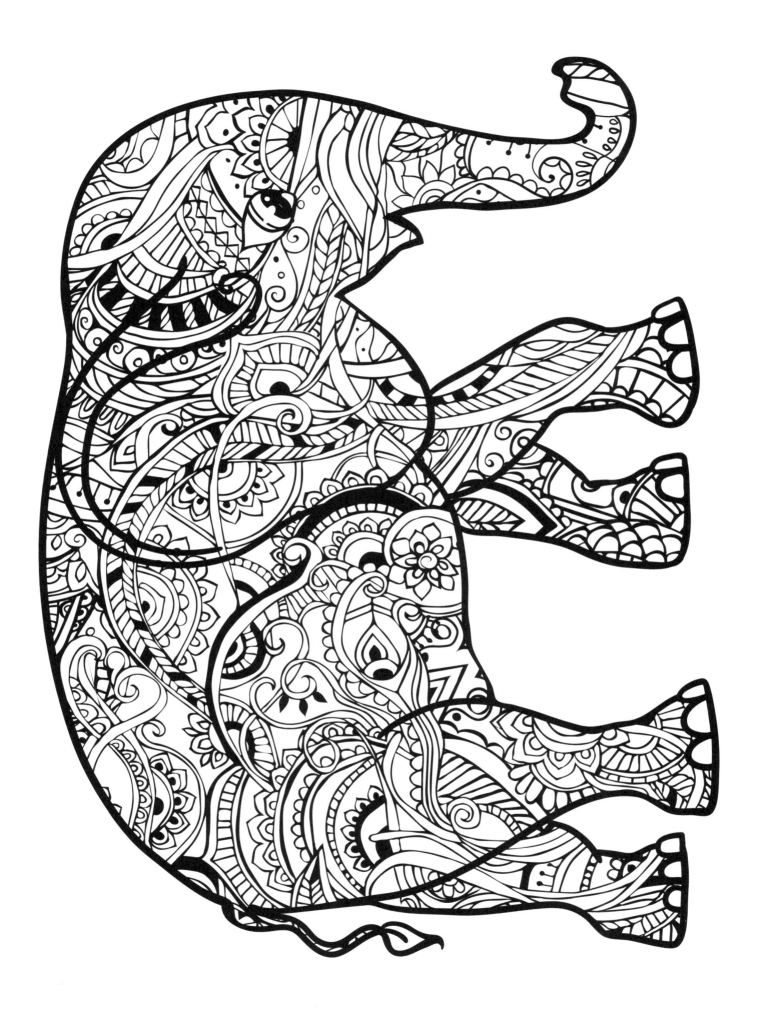

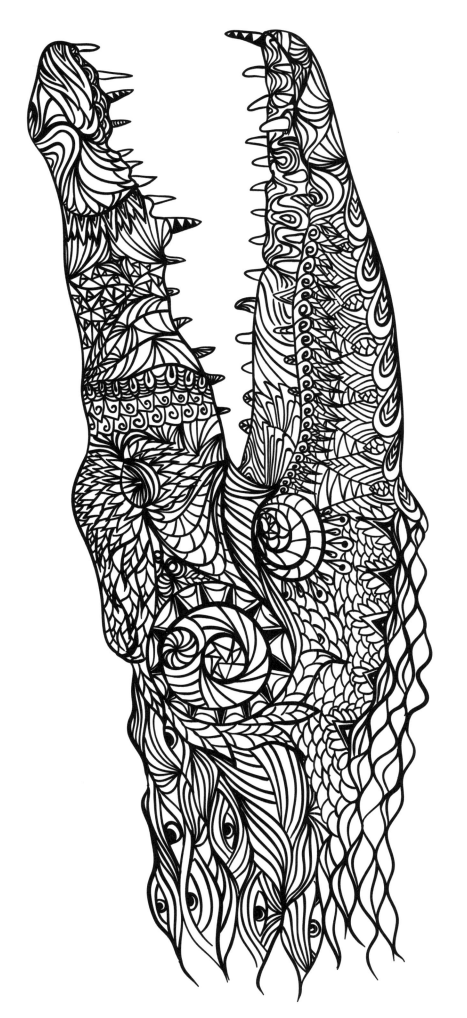

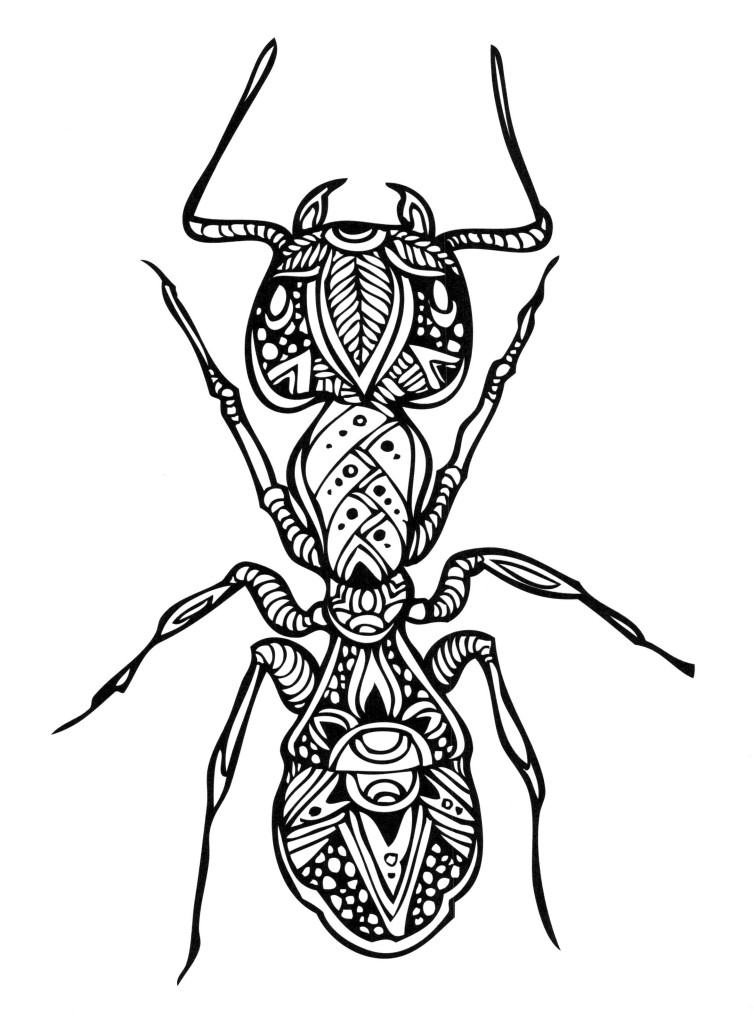

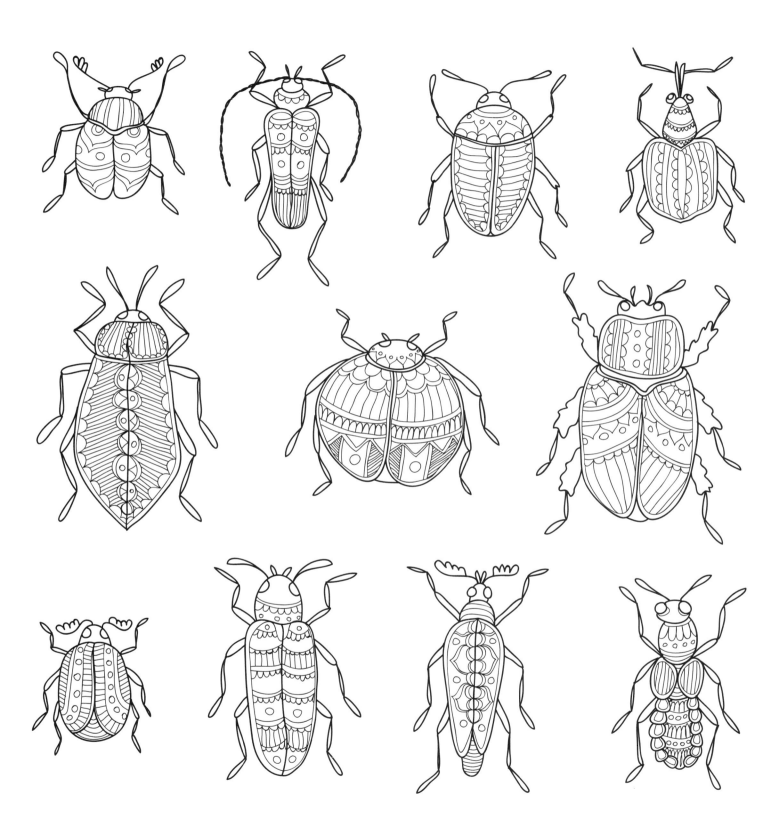

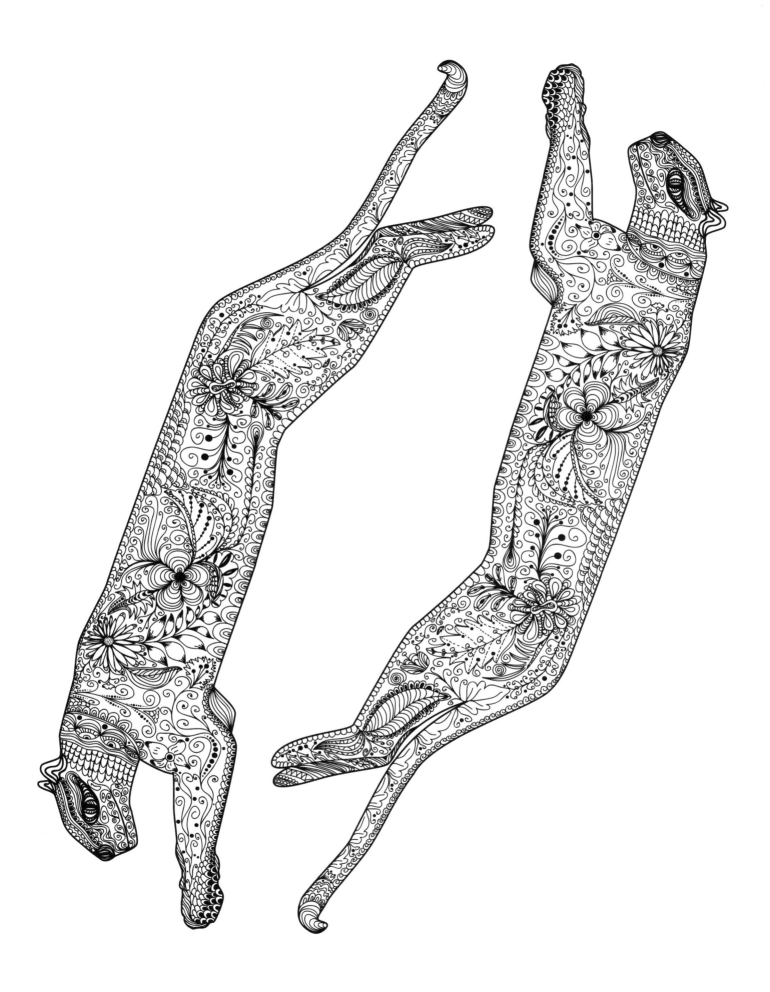

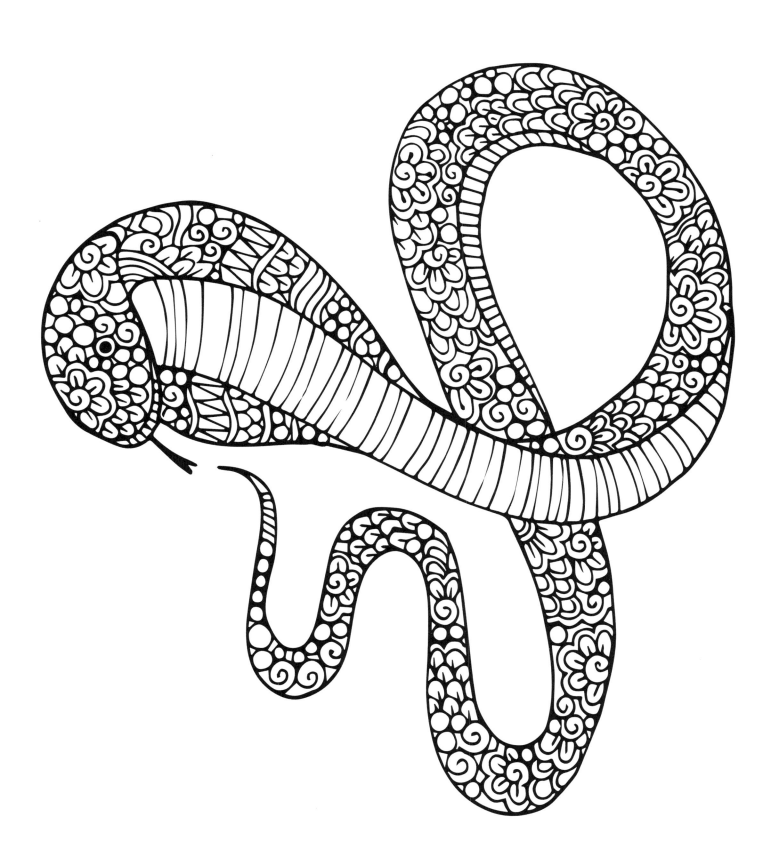

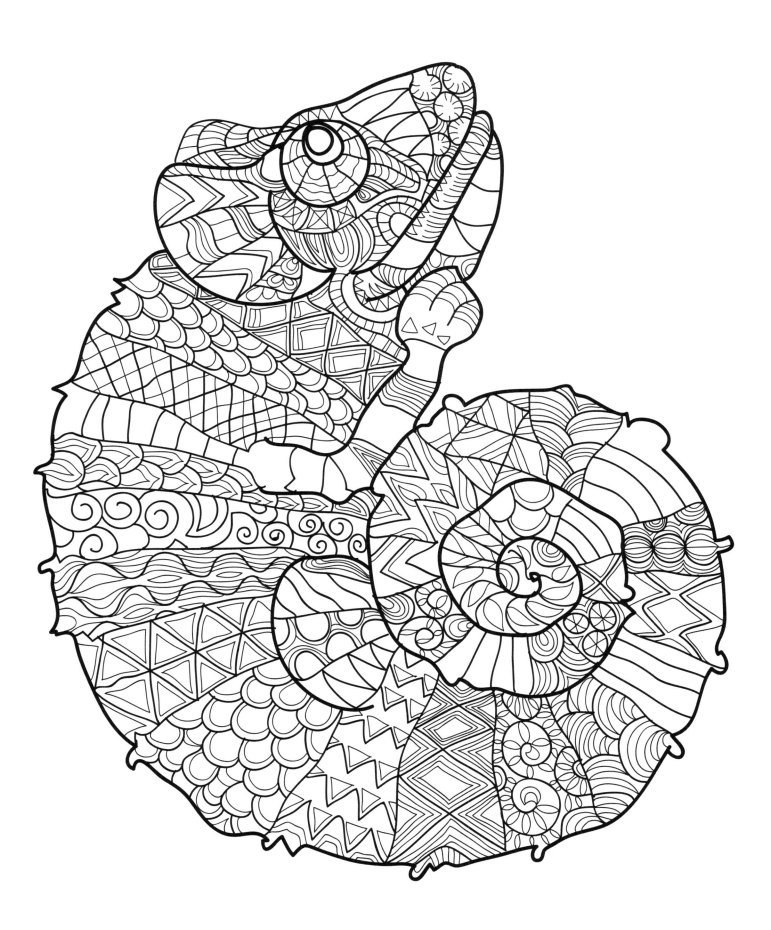

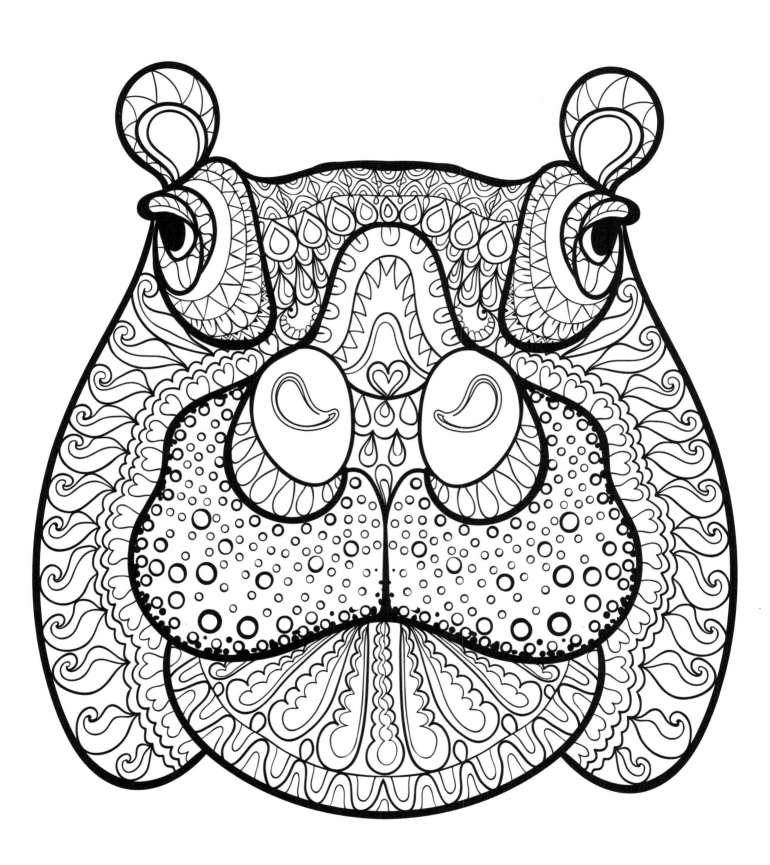

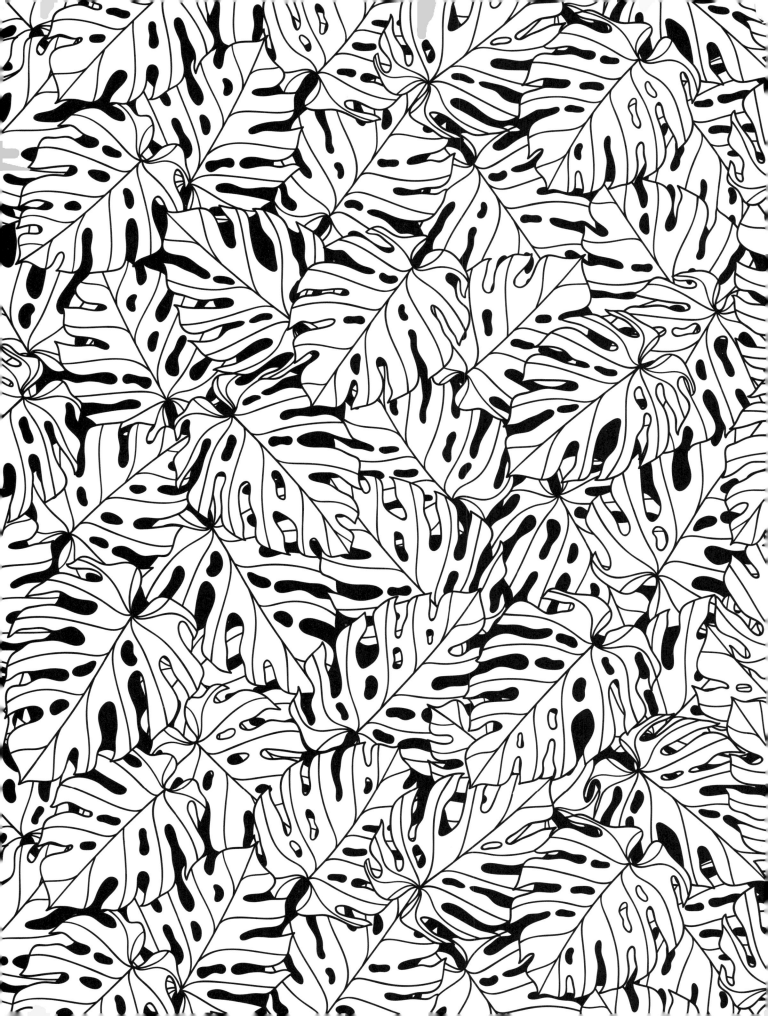

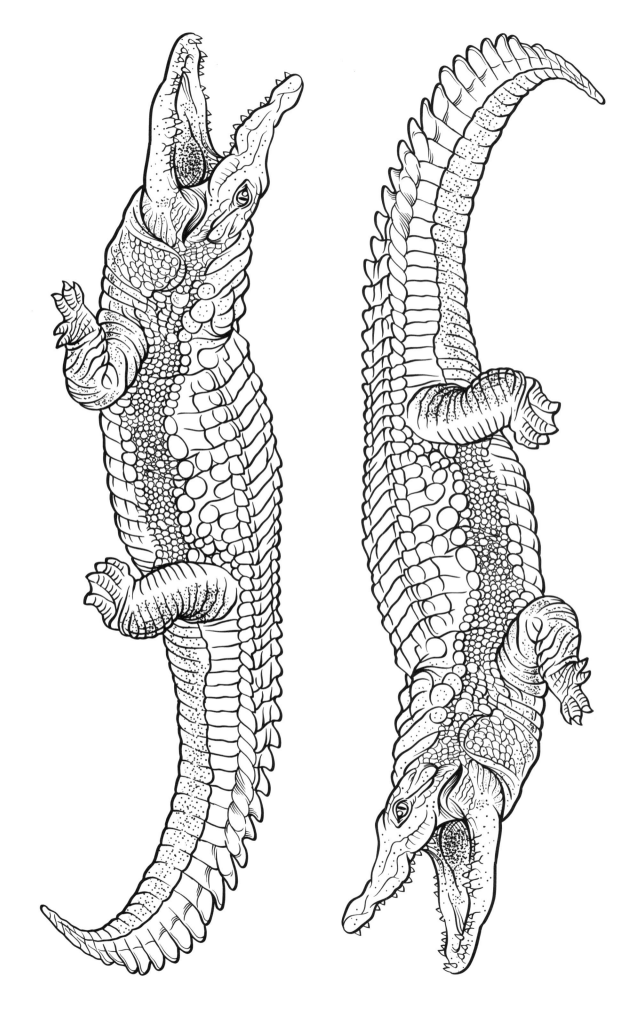

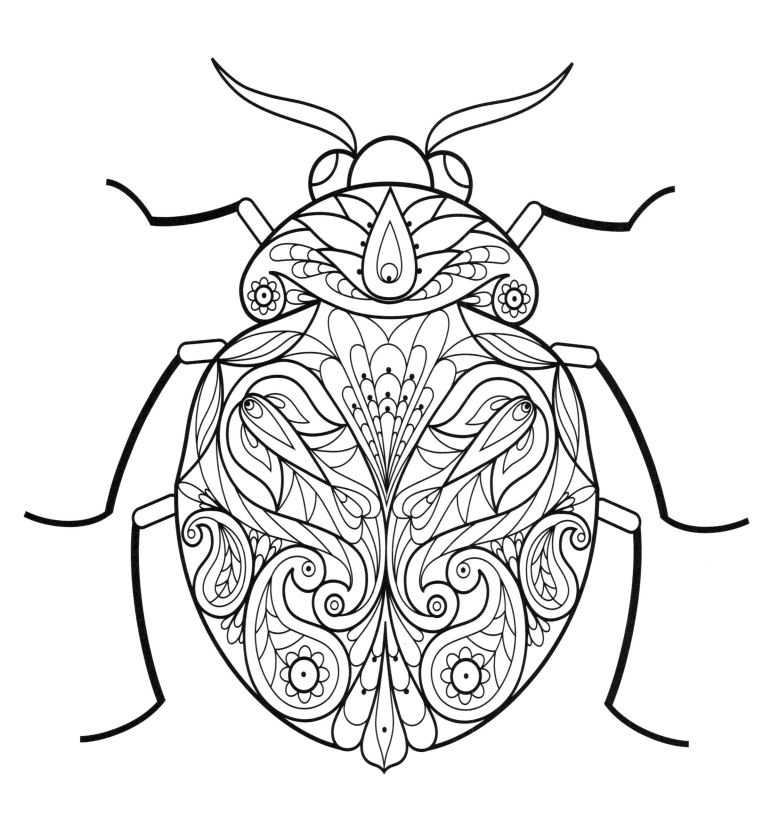

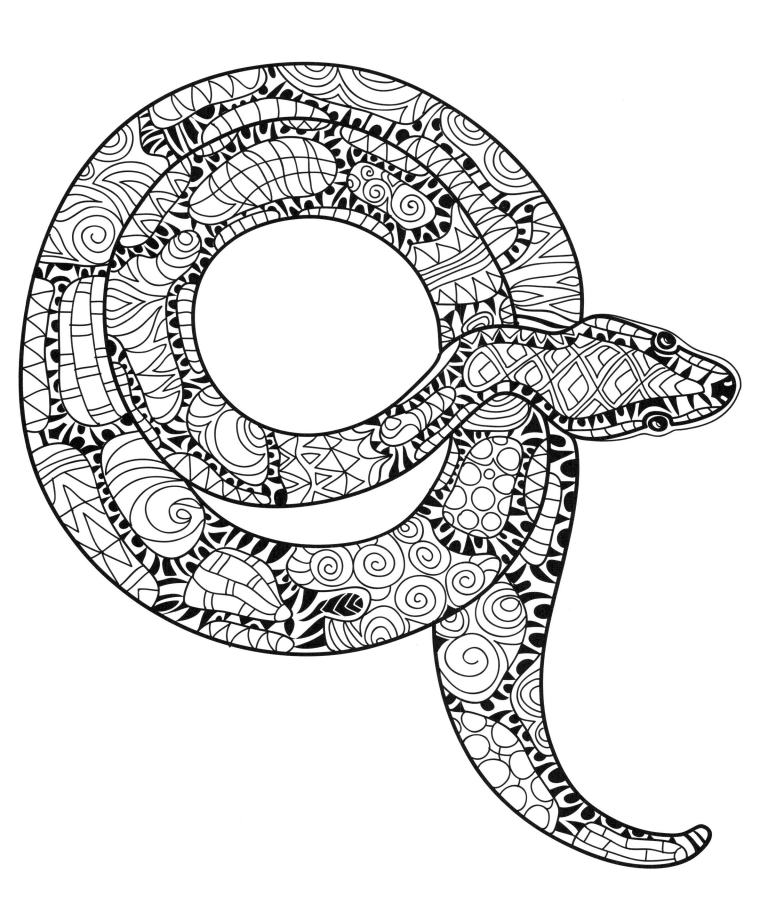

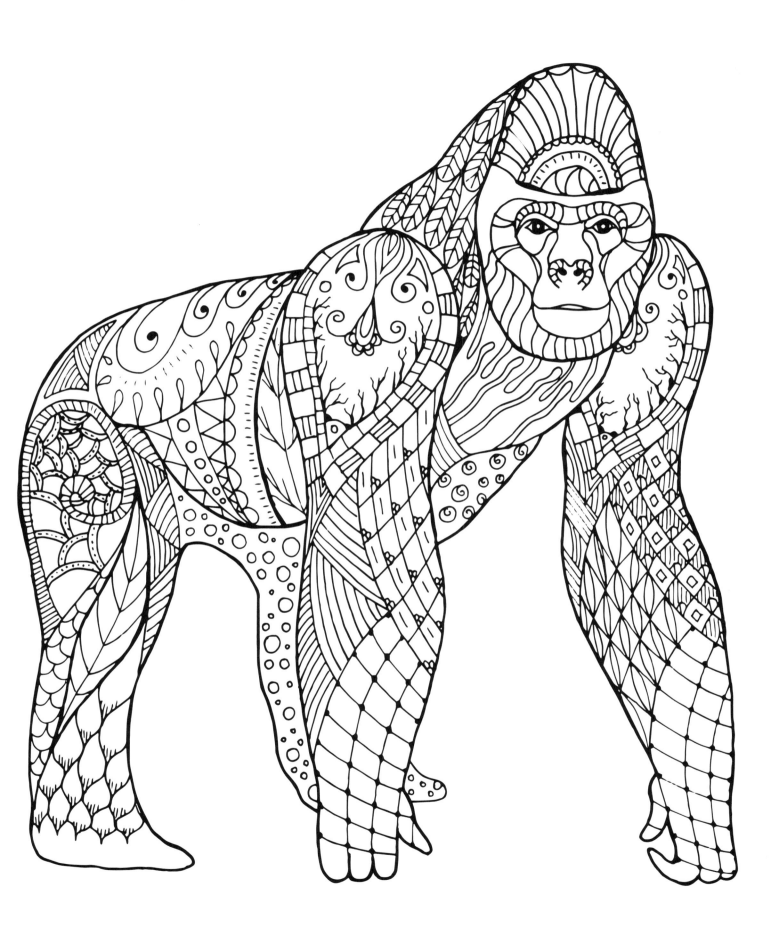

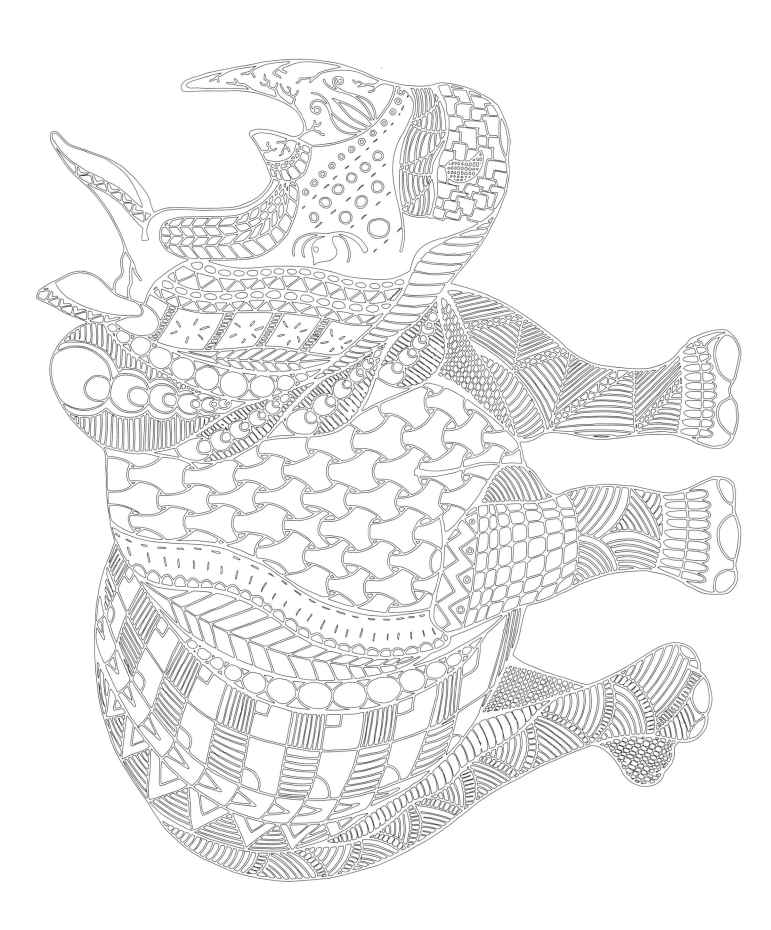

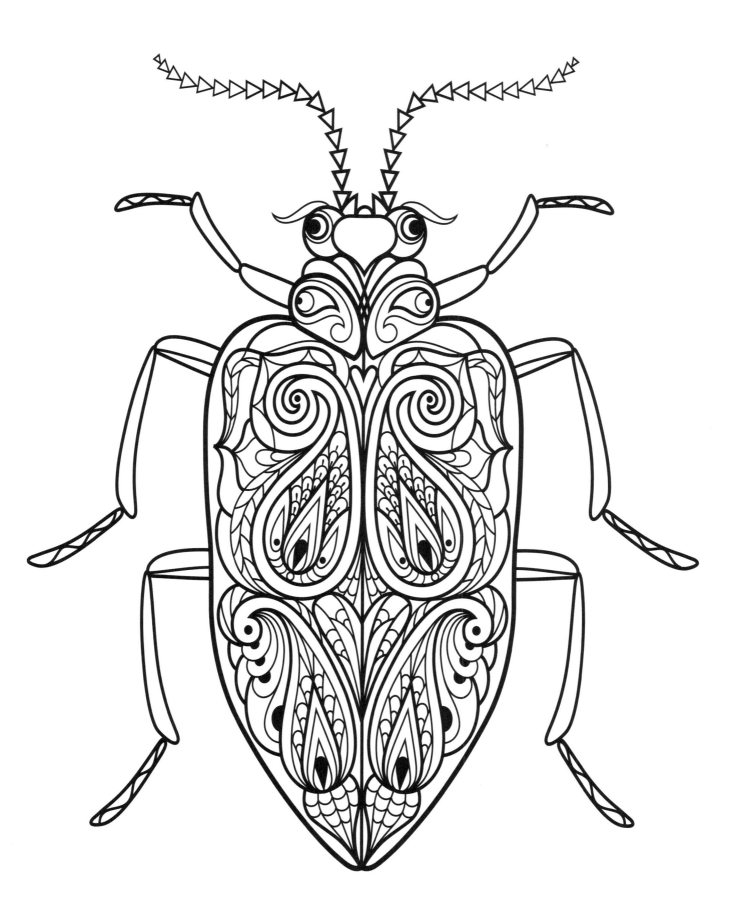

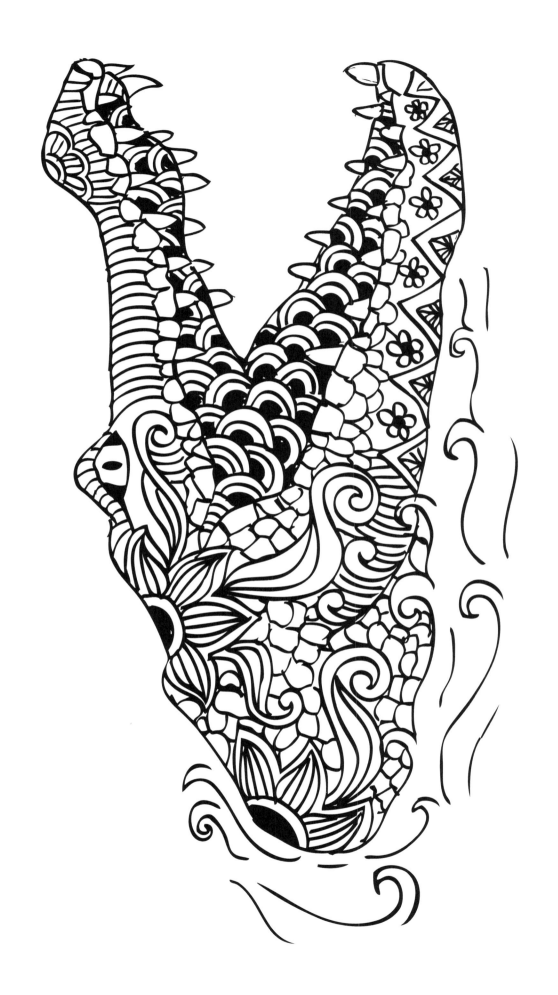

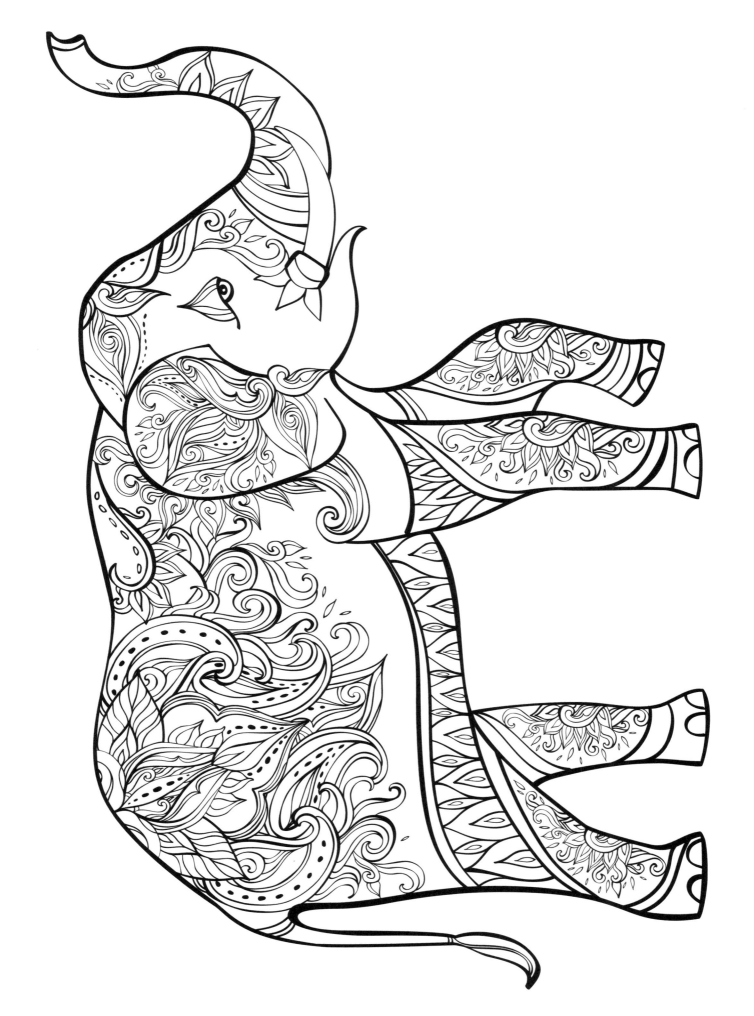

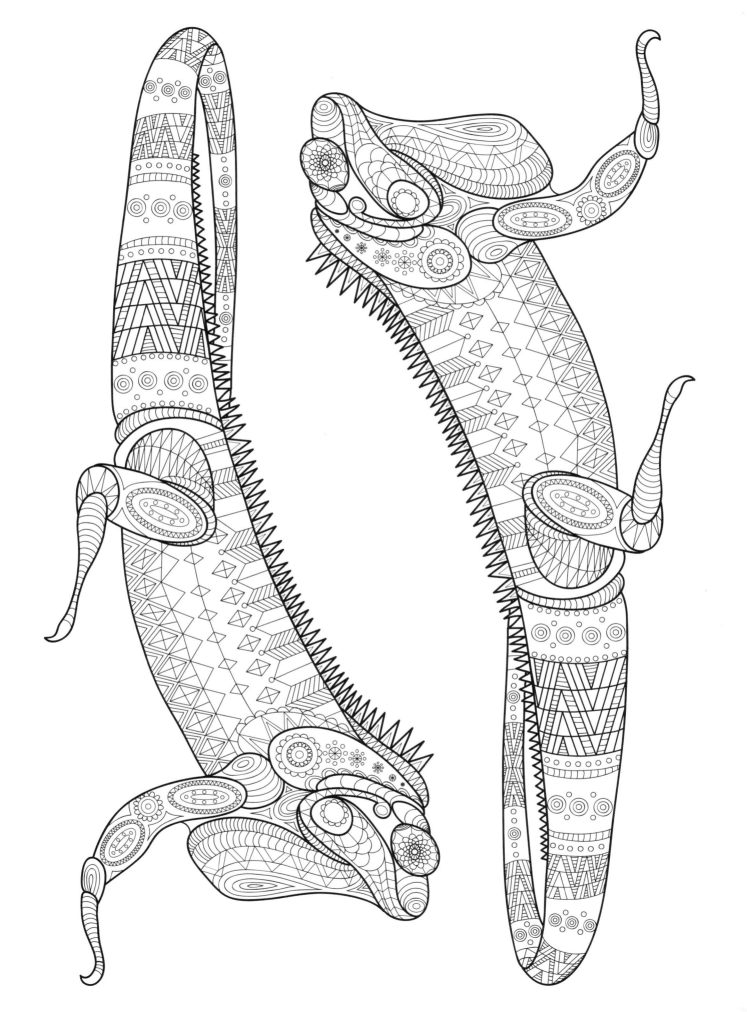

THIS IS A CARLTON BOOK

Published by Carlton Books Ltd
20 Mortimer Street
London W1T 3JW

Copyright © 2016 Carlton Books Ltd

A CIP catalogue record for this book is available from the British Library

10 9 8 7 6 5 4 3 2 1

ISBN 978-1-78097-862-8

Printed in China

Picture credits: Shutterstock.com